The Extraordinary Adventures
of Mr Benn

# Caveman

Based on the TV series
by David McKee

HODDER AND STOUGHTON
LONDON SYDNEY AUCKLAND

British Library Cataloguing in Publication Data
A catalogue record for this book is available from the British Library

ISBN 0 340 58990 6 (cased)
ISBN 0 340 58997 3 (limp)

Text copyright © David McKee 1993
Illustrations copyright © King Rollo Films Ltd 1993

The rights of David McKee to be identified as the author of the text of this work and of
King Rollo Films Ltd to be identified as the illustrator of this work have been asserted
by them in accordance with the Copyright, Designs and Patent Act 1988.

Cased edition first published 1993
Picture Knight edition first published 1993

Published by Hodder and Stoughton Children's Books,
a division of Hodder and Stoughton Ltd,
Mill Road, Dunton Green, Sevenoaks, Kent TN13 2YA

Printed in Singapore

Festive Road was usually very quiet but on this
morning, the street was crowded with traffic.
At number 52 Mr Benn looked out of his window
at all the traffic.
"What's going on?" he asked a man.
"The main road is being repaired and it's the rush
hour," said the man. "All the traffic has to come
this way."

Mr Benn walked back inside and sat down to look at the television. He watched a film about cavemen. It said that cavemen lived a long time ago. They lived in caves which was why they were called cavemen. They dressed in furs and worked with tools made out of stone. Mr Benn was very interested but the traffic outside was so noisy that he couldn't really hear the television.

"I must get away from all this noise," he said, and he thought about the special costume shop that he knew, the shop where adventures could start from. "That's the place to go," he smiled.

Mr Benn was soon in the lane with the shop. He paused for a moment outside, then went in.
He looked at the costumes. "Something away from cars," he thought.

As if by magic the shopkeeper appeared.
"Good morning, sir," he said.
"Good morning," said Mr Benn. "Is this a caveman's outfit?"
"Yes," said the shopkeeper. "They used to live in caves, you know. They didn't have houses."

"They didn't have any cars either," said Mr Benn.
"Do you think I might try it on?"
He took the fur into the changing room.
Once inside he quickly changed. He smiled at the furry
Mr Benn in the mirror and then went through the door
that could lead to an adventure.

On the other side of the door everything was very dark. Mr Benn could see a light ahead and walked towards it. As it became lighter, he found himself walking out of a cave.
In front of him were other caves and lots of people dressed in furs.

Mr Benn went over to a patch of grass and lay down.
He closed his eyes and thought how peaceful it was.
The sun was shining.
"I wonder why the cave people don't lie out here.
It's lovely," he thought.
It wasn't long before he knew why.

From a long way off came a rumbling noise. At the same time, the cave people started to shout.
In the distance was a great cloud of dust coming closer and closer.
The cavemen were shouting, "Look out!" and "Get out of the way!" and "Run for it!"

Mr Benn jumped to his feet and raced back to the caves just as a huge animal thundered past.

"Golly!" said Mr Benn. "What was that?"
"A dinosaur," said a man. "Every morning the
dinosaurs rush past here on their way to get to the best
feeding places. And now it is the evening so they race
back to get the best places to sleep. We never get a
moment's peace."
Suddenly there was a crash and the dinosaurs screeched
to a halt. Some of the dinosaurs had fallen over,
blocking the road.
"That's always happening," said the man.
"They're so impatient, no manners at all."
And with that the dinosaurs picked themselves up and
rushed off again.

The cave people settled down to their supper.
Mr Benn asked: "Why do you stay here? There must be other places to live away from the dinosaurs."
"Not with caves," said the man. "And we need caves to live in."

When the meal was over, everyone went to their own caves to sleep. Mr Benn settled down under a pile of furs for the night.

The next morning when Mr Benn woke up, he heard shouting outside the cave. He looked out and saw some men trying to move a dinosaur.
"Can I help?" asked Mr Benn.
"This often happens," explained a man. "An animal just parks here to sleep and blocks the entrance of a cave so that people can't get out.
Help us push it out of the way, will you?"
So Mr Benn got behind the dinosaur and pushed and heaved it out of the way.

When Mr Benn was having his breakfast, he heard the rumbling noise again. This time he knew what to expect. Sure enough, the animals went rushing past but this time in the opposite direction, off in search of food.

When all the dinosaurs had gone, Mr Benn asked if they could go for a walk to get away from the dust.
"Yes, we'll all go," said the others, "and show you around. You have to be careful crossing the dinosaur road. The dinosaurs don't mean any harm but they are clumsy and if one does bump into you, it can be quite nasty."

They looked first one way, then the other. A large cloud of dust was approaching. They waited until the dinosaur had passed. This time when they looked the road was clear, so they crossed. But they kept looking each way in case a dinosaur should suddenly appear.

But none did.

As they walked on, the countryside became greener.
There were trees and streams, and the air was fresh.
The children played freely and everyone was much
happier.

"This is where we would really like to live," said one of the men.
"Why don't you?" asked Mr Benn.
"Because there are no caves, silly," the man laughed.
"Build some, or at least something that will do instead," said Mr Benn. "I'll show you how to build stone huts. First we'll need a lot of very large stones."

Mr Benn showed them how to place the stones one
on top of the other. As soon as the cave people saw
how it was done, they started to build several huts.

When the walls were finished, Mr Benn took them
into the woods to get some branches for the roofs.
Next they cut pieces of turf from the ground, then
laid the turf on the branches.

Lo and behold, the houses were complete!
The people were very pleased.
"From now on we can live here," they agreed.

A man appeared beside Mr Benn.
"Come and look inside this hut, sir," he said.

Just then, Mr Benn heard a noise in the distance. The cave people were standing on top of a hill. They were watching the dinosaurs' rush hour again. After the dinosaurs had gone, Mr Benn went into the hut and, just as he had expected, he found himself back in the changing room of the shop. He took a last look at himself and then changed back into his own clothes.

Back in the shop Mr Benn returned the fur outfit to the
shopkeeper and said, "Thank you very, very much."
"Thank you, sir," said the shopkeeper. "We look forward
to seeing you again."
As Mr Benn waved goodbye from the door he said,
"I look forward to seeing you again. Goodbye."

Mr Benn walked back along Festive Road which was
still filled with cars and lorries.
"Somehow they seem different now," thought
Mr Benn, and for a moment he imagined that they
looked like dinosaurs.

At his gate Mr Benn realised that he was holding
something in his hand. It was a stone hammer.
"I wonder how long I've been holding that," he
thought. "I'll keep it. It's just what I need to help
me remember."